Dedicated to all parents.

Warner Books, Inc., 1271 Avenue of the Americas, New York, NY 10020

 A Time Warner Company

Printed in Italy
First Printing: August 1994
10 9 8 7 6 5 4 3 2 1

Library of Congress Cataloging-in-Publication Data
Randall, Brian.
The B book / Brian Randall.
p.   cm.
ISBN 0-446-51801-8
I. Title.
PS3568. A4894B18 1994
818'.5407--dc20   93-40927
                                            CIP

THE B BOOK

BY BRIAN RANDALL

WARNER BOOKS

A Time Warner Company

See suburban Sunnyview,

Seems pleasant enough-friendly too.

Let's zoom in for a closer view.

Who's awake at ten to eight?
Yippee!
It's little Miss Bee.

I can tell when the sun looks

my way,

That it's going to be a

beautiful day.

Mr. Sun, Mr. Sun,

Where's my Daddy, Pop?

(sniff)

How can this be?

Daddy leaves home

without me.

There goes Dad

off to the company.

He's not the boss.

He says Yes-Yes a lot.

I'll never say Yes-Yes.

I'll build my own company.

The B Company—

named after me.

I'll start from the bottom

and work up to more.

B SHOES on each foot

a foot in each door.

On to the top

B-DO's!

Why not?

The choice is yours —

Drive B or B not.

Cars, trucks, planes galore.

More! More! More! More!

Spread the word

from East to West...

B is Bigger, Biggest, Best!

FILMS

REAL ESTATE

DEFENSE

AIRLINES

BUILDING

OIL

RADAR

HAIR

FASHIONS

STEREO

INSURANCE

BBB·TV

SHOES

BROADCAST

TRAVEL

B

TECHNOLOGY

SPACE

S   U   C   C

E   S   S   .

My employees love me,

they call me <u>friend</u>.

They even dress like me.

What?

What did you say?

You shut up!

Do it my way.

Push those papers!

Push those pens!

You can never work too much.
My company has that personal touch.

The land, the sky, the sea,

It all belongs

to **ME.**

The LAND   The SKY   The SEA

What's Mine is Mine.

All **Mine.**

If you try to take it away...

...you'll die.

But I'm alone.

I'm depressed.

Miss B's
Rise to the Top

LIFE
EXCLUSIVE

LIFE

I'm such a big mess.

Who will cry when I die?

No one… no one…

Not even Mr. Sun.

I see the future...

Disaster. Disease.

I'll change, I promise...

Please! Please!

Wake up, Bee.

If you want friends,

and a brand-new you,

We have a lot of work to do.

So Bee,
what's it going to be?

GREED

or is it...

CHARITY

...Nothing makes you more content
than giving 100%.

You mean donate all my bucks?

Mr. Sun, you're nuts!

Citizens! Citizens!

I'm raising your taxes 200%.

CRACK!   BO

OM! CRASH!

You rotten, wretched brat.

Cover the entire world

In shadow deep and black.

B must fall.

B's the one.

She stole away our sun.

Man, woman, child
shed tears of despair...

...fear turns to anger...
anarchy lights the air.

REVOLUTION

I better run...

better hide...

better better hurry...

They know my face,

No place is safe.

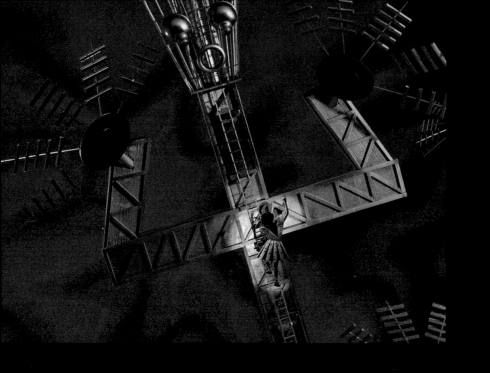

HELP

...Ahhhhhhhhhhhhhhhhhhhhhh, GULP!

Come Bee,

     Here you are safe.

This is where

     your destiny waits.

Before your rise

Before your fall…

...was a time called Paradise.

Look what is before you

Don't let it slip away...

Home sweet home is waiting

At the end of your long day.

Daddy, Daddy,

I've learned so much today.

Thank you, Mr. Sun,

For showing me the way.

THE **B** BOOK

was made possible with
a lot of help from my friends.

THE B BOOK

written and directed by
Brian Randall

The Crew

✳

photographers
Robert Jacobs, *principal*
David Sawyer
Brian Randall
Bill McCullom

✳

art assistants
Pat Place
Margo Sawyer
Mary Vengrofski
Anthony Lombardo
Pamela Hanna
David Csicsko
Michael Dal Cerro
Greg Metz
Susannah Irwin
Paul Niski
Natalie Kitamura
Jonathan Greenblatt

Art, Sets & Design

Brian Randall

✳

editors
Karen Kelly
Lois Jensen
Janet Jensen
Lyn Siefert

✳

design
The B Company, LA
Michelle Chang
Fang Fang Ho

✳

typography
Michelle Chang

The Cast

✳

Little Miss Bee is
Mary Vengrofski

✳

Mr. Sun is
David Sawyer

✳

Dad is
James Fox

✳

B Employees
Michael Gilberto
Janet & Lois Jensen
Margo Sawyer

✳

costumes
Brian Randall
Carrie Hollister

✳

hair and make-up
Carrie Hollister

Thank you,
Laurence Kirshbaum, Karen Kelly, Jackie Meyer, & Milton Batalion.
Anthony Lombardo, Kimberly Witherspoon, Ursula Randall, Margo Sawyer, & Susan Grode.
Ross Elhert Photo Lab, Chicago, IL, & Ross Typographic Service, Inc., S. Pasadena, CA.

...another fine product from The B Company, LA